Dedicated to my mother who taught us to love nature and my sister, Julie, who carries on her work.

There's a programme on the tele'
And the man told us it's true
That everyone must stay inside,
It was the same the whole world through.

As you grow, you might forget
And it's something you'll be told:
How we all learned 'Lockdown lessons'
When the world was put on hold.

For weeks, I had to stay at home
And my house became quite small.
Far and wide, children felt the same
We're just one world after all.

Before the Lockdown happened
The Earth was in a mess.
We saw Mother Nature's problems
And found her in distress.

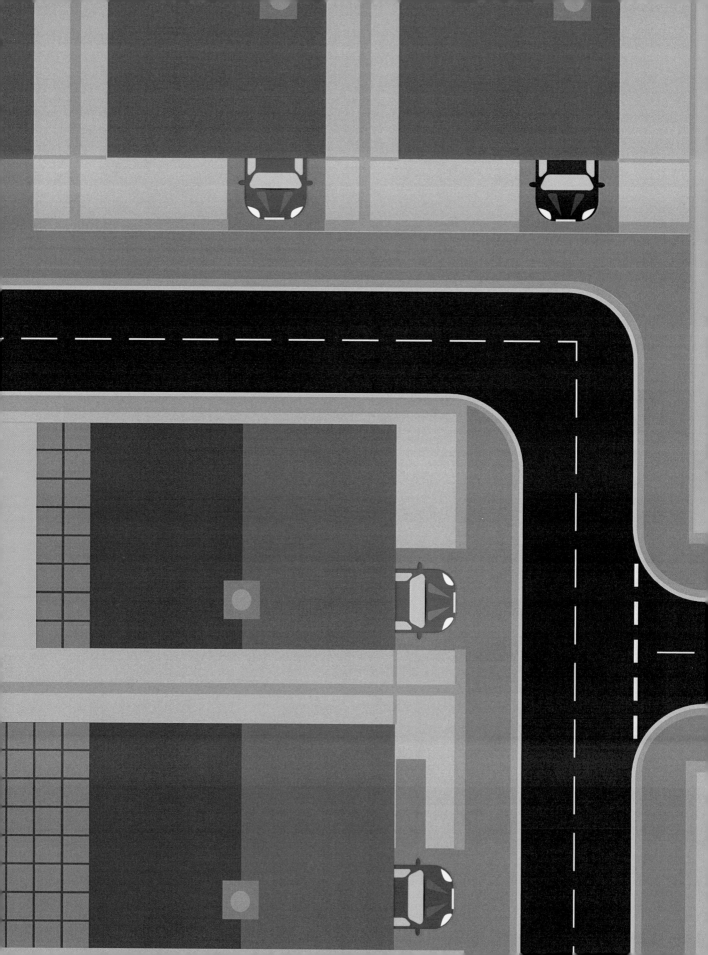

People had been dropping litter
They'd dumped plastic in our seas
They paved our gardens and our meadows
And they'd cut down precious trees.

In the lockdown streets, the noise had stopped
In the skies, not a single plane.
If you listened you could hear the whispers:
'The Earth is recovering again.'

And across the world, it happened,
When we were stuck inside for days;
New life sprung up everywhere
Because humans had changed their ways.

Now Mum left her car at home
And our walk became a treat.
I switched off the TV, put down the phone;
Enjoyed green grass beneath my feet.

Nature became my teacher
And her lessons were really good
She asked us to live a different way
I'm just one child who thinks we should.

I looked up in the trees for answers
A robin told me what she'd heard:
'People must learn to share this world.'
She was a wise and clever bird.

'The natural world's been struggling
We need more butterflies and bees
Let's stop mowing wild flowers
Let's stop chopping down ancient trees.'

I learnt insects have a job to do
And we should simply let them pass
Not spray their food with chemicals
And replace their homes with plastic grass.

If the fish in streams and rivers
Could tell me what they'd seen
They'd say: 'In Lockdown, there was much less litter
Which made the water clean.'

All pond life needs protection:
The tadpoles, frogs and toads.
People can't keep building on our woodlands
Wildlife can't live on concrete roads!

If you could only talk to animals
Then you would know just what to do
Across the world, nature needs your help
Its future relies on...

You!

HEDGEHOGS WELCOME

So get outdoors, plant flowers and trees
Look after creatures everywhere;
Feed birds, save endangered animals
And really show you care.

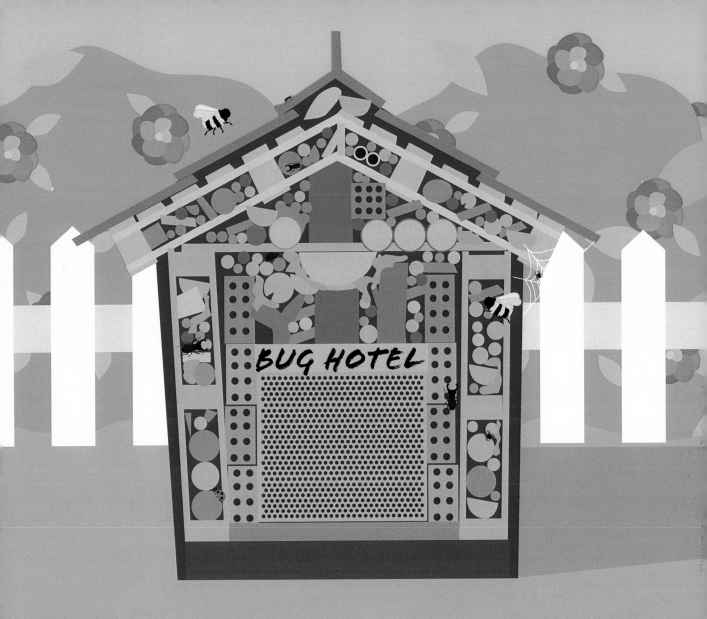

This planet is full of wonder
And it's time to take a proper look
Nature shouldn't be a history lesson
On the pages of a book.

In 2020, the climate changed
And I'm not talking about the weather
Children realised we have 'just one world'
And we must protect the Earth...